JOHNNY APPLESEED

Johnny Appleseed
and Other Poems
by
Vachel Lindsay

Illustrated by
George Richards

New York
The Macmillan Company

FOREWORD

THE title for this selection of Vachel Lindsay's poems naturally uses the name of his Great American, Johnny Appleseed. Lindsay the hero-worshipper, the preacher, the dreamer, the glorifier of Springfield, Illinois, the banner-waver and drum-beater for all true Springfields and a great American highway connecting them—that is one Lindsay. He knows how to put the essence of an American's ideas about the pioneer ("The Santa-Fé Trail"), the sower ("Johnny Appleseed"), the circus ("The Kallyope Yell"), into booming, singing rhythms for the human voice to speak again. The virtue of his strange, emotional story-poems is in their simplicity, in their use of general ideas in mind pictures that young people can understand, and in the primitive climaxes of rhythm.

One recalls Lindsay striding about, turning an indifferent, self-conscious audience into a single-mooded mob, singing his refrains. In contrast are his lyrics. Seldom in poetry has there been so charming and also powerful a conception, as that of the "Moon Poems." And what delicate humor in "A Dirge for a Righteous Kitten," "Crickets on a Strike," "The Little Turtle," etc. What exquisite simplicity in "The Flower of Mending."

Many thousands of young people who know Lindsay personally are reading and writing poetry because he stirred them first to a feeling of the possibility of words in rhythmic pattern. These boys and girls are in high schools all over America, or in isolated villages where he tramped, "preaching the gospel of beauty," exchanging a reading or a new poem for his food and lodging.

Other children are using many of the poems for poem-dances, demonstrating that connection, newly discovered, or rather, recently acted upon, between physical rhythmic motion and word sense. Children particularly love "The Potatoes' Dance," "The King of Yellow Butterflies," "The Chinese Nightingale." Some of them have acted out the longer poems very dramatically and with beautiful settings.

This book is for all boys and girls who love poetry already. They will find all their Lindsay favorites here in a convenient size to carry about and learn by heart. It is also, especially, for those many unfortunate youngsters who think they don't like poetry. We think this book will convert them, if any book in the world can. If only they could have seen Lindsay himself, or one of his rare imitators, do the thing right!

Beyond its importance as the first official selection from Lindsay for boys and girls, it is also an unusual record of a rare friendship. The publisher who writes this note can recall few collaborations as happy as this. George Mather Richards and Nicholas Vachel Lindsay were friends in art school in New York many years ago. Today they are as close as ever, though separated by a continent. No poem must go in that Richards does not approve, and any picture he does is perfect, though the author himself is the only person, hitherto, to illustrate his poems. His own pictures, and his theories about them, will interest older boys and girls, and can be found in his Collected Poems, Revised and Illustrated Edition, 1925.

CONTENTS

PART I

YELLOW BUTTERFLIES

PART II

MOON POEMS

PART IV

NIGHTINGALES

PART I
YELLOW BUTTERFLIES

The Sorceress!

I asked her, "Is Aladdin's lamp
Hidden anywhere?"
"Look into your heart," she said,
"Aladdin's lamp is there."

She took my heart with glowing hands.
It burned to dust and air
And smoke and rolling thistledown
Blowing everywhere.

"Follow the thistledown," she said,
"Till doomsday, if you dare,
Over the hills and far away.
Aladdin's lamp is there."

The Little Turtle

(A Recitation for Martha Wakefield, Three Years Old)

There was a little turtle.
He lived in a box.
He swam in a puddle.
He climbed on the rocks.

He snapped at a mosquito.
He snapped at a flea.
He snapped at a minnow.
And he snapped at me.

He caught the mosquito.
He caught the flea.
He caught the minnow.
But he didn't catch me.

A Dirge for a Righteous Kitten

(To be intoned, all but the two italicized lines, which are to be spoken in a snappy, matter-of-fact way)

Ding-dong, ding-dong, ding-dong.
Here lies a kitten good, who kept
A kitten's proper place.
He stole no pantry eatables,
Nor scratched the baby's face.
He let the alley-cats alone.
He had no yowling vice.
His shirt was always laundried well,
He freed the house of mice.
Until his death he had not caused
His little mistress tears,
He wore his ribbon prettily,
He washed behind his ears.
Ding-dong, ding-dong, ding-dong.

The Mysterious Cat

(A chant for a children's pantomime dance, suggested by a
picture painted by George Mather Richards)

I saw a proud, mysterious cat,
I saw a proud, mysterious cat,
Too proud to catch a mouse or rat—
Mew, mew, mew.

But catnip she would eat, and purr,
But catnip she would eat, and purr.
And goldfish she did much prefer—
Mew, mew, mew.

I saw a cat—'twas but a dream,
I saw a cat—'twas but a dream
Who scorned the slave that brought her cream—
Mew, mew, mew.

Unless the slave were dressed in style,
Unless the slave were dressed in style,
And knelt before her all the while—
Mew, mew, mew.

Did you ever hear of a thing like that?

6

Did you ever hear of a thing like that?
Did you ever hear of a thing like that?
Oh, what a proud, mysterious cat.
Oh, what a proud, mysterious cat.
Oh, what a proud, mysterious cat.
Mew . . . mew . . . mew.

Two old crows sat on a fence rail.
Two old crows sat on a fence rail,
Thinking of effect and cause,
Of weeds and flowers,
And nature's laws.
One of them muttered, one of them stuttered,
One of them stuttered, one of them muttered.
Each of them thought far more than he uttered.
One crow asked the other crow a riddle.
One crow asked the other crow a riddle:
The muttering crow
Asked the stuttering crow,
"Why does a bee have a sword to his fiddle?
Why does a bee have a sword to his fiddle?"
"Bee-cause," said the other crow,
"Bee-cause,
B B B B B B B B B B B B B B B-cause."
Just then a bee flew close to their rail:—
"Buzzzzzzzzzzzzzzzzzz   zzzzzzzzz zzzzzzzzzzzzzzz
    ZZZZZZZZ."
And those two black crows
Turned pale,
And away those crows did sail.
Why?
B B B B B B B B B B B B B B B-cause.
B B B B B B B B B B B B B B B-cause.
"Buzzzzzzzzzzzzzzzzzz   zzzzzzzzz zzzzzzzzzzzzzzz
    ZZZZZZZZ.'

An Explanation of the Grasshopper

The Grasshopper, the grasshopper,
I will explain to you:—
He is the Brownies' racehorse,
The fairies' Kangaroo.

The Lion

The Lion is a kingly beast.
He likes a Hindu for a feast.
And if no Hindu he can get,
The lion-family is upset.

He cuffs his wife and bites her ears
Till she is nearly moved to tears.
Then some explorer finds the den
And all is family peace again.

The Dandelion

O dandelion, rich and haughty,
King of village flowers!
Each day is coronation time,
You have no humble hours.
I like to see you bring a troop
To beat the blue-grass spears,
To scorn the lawn-mower that would be
Like fate's triumphant shears,
Your yellow heads are cut away,
It seems your reign is o'er.
By noon you raise a sea of stars
More golden than before.

The Lame Boy and the Fairy

(To the rhythm of Chopin's Berceuse)

A lame boy
Met a fairy
In a meadow
Where the bells grow.

And the fairy
Kissed him gaily.

And the fairy
Gave him friendship,
Gave him healing,
Gave him wings.

"All the fashions
I will give you.
You will fly, dear,
All the long year.

"Wings of springtime,
Wings of summer,
Wings of autumn,
Wings of winter!

"Here is
A dress for springtime."
And she gave him
A dress of grasses,
Orchard blossoms,
Wild-flowers found in
Mountain passes,
*Shoes of song and
Wings of rhyme.*

16

"Here is
A dress for summer."
And she gave him
A hat of sunflowers,
A suit of poppies,
Clover, daisies,
All from wheat-sheaves
In harvest time;
Shoes of song and
Wings of rhyme.

"Here is
A dress for autumn."
And she gave him
A suit of red haw,
Hickory, apple,
Elder, pawpaw,
Maple, hazel,
Elm and grape leaves,
And blue
And white
Cloaks of smoke,
And veils of sunlight,
From the Indian summer prime!
Shoes of song and
Wings of rhyme.

"Here is
A dress for winter."
And she gave him
A polar bear suit,
And he heard the
Christmas horns toot,
And she gave him

Green festoons and
Red balloons and
All the sweet cakes
And the snowflakes
Of Christmas time,
Shoes of song and
Wings of rhyme.

And the fairy
Kept him laughing,
Led him dancing,
Kept him climbing
On the hilltops
Toward the moon.

"We shall see silver ships.
We shall see singing ships,
Valleys of spray today,
Mountains of foam.
We have been long away,
Far from our wonderland.
Here come the ships of love
Taking us home.

"Who are our captains bold?
They are the saints of old.
One is Saint Christopher.
He takes your hand.
He leads the cloudy fleet.
He gives us bread and meat.
His is our ship till
We reach our dear land.

"Where is our house to be?
Far in the ether sea.

There where the North Star
Is moored in the deep.
Sleepy old comets nod
There on the silver sod.
Sleepy young fairy flowers
Laugh in their sleep.

"A hundred years
And
A day,
There we will fly
And play
I-spy and *cross-tag*.
And meet on the highway,
And call to the game
Little Red Riding Hood,
Goldilocks, Santa Claus,
Every beloved
And heart-shaking name."

And the lame child
And the fairy
Journeyed far, far
To the North Star.

The Fairy from the Apple-Seed

O apple-seed I planted in a silly shallow place
In a bowl of wrought silver, with Sangamon earth within
    it,
O baby tree that came, without an apple on it,
A tree that grew a tiny height, but thickened on apace,
With bossy glossy arms, and leaves of trembling lace.

One night the trunk was rent, and the heavy bowl rocked
    round,
The boughs were bending here and there, with a curious
    locust sound,
And a tiny dryad came, from out the doll tree,
And held the boughs in ivory hands,
And waved her black hair round,
And climbed, and ate with merry words
The sudden fruit it bore.
And in the leaves she hides and sings
And guards my study door.

She guards it like a watchdog true
And robbers run away.
For hearts of oak, by flying beauty swayed:—
It is the cross-roads
Resurrection
Parade.

The flags are big, like rainbows flashing round,
They spread like sails, and lift us from the ground,
Star-born ships, that have come in masquerade:—
It is the cross-roads
Resurrection
Parade.

Crickets on a Strike

The foolish queen of fairyland
From her milk-white throne in a lily-bell,
Gave command to her cricket-band
To play for her when the dew-drops fell.

But the cold dew spoiled their instruments
And they play for the foolish queen no more.
Instead those sturdy malcontents
Play sharps and flats in my kitchen floor.

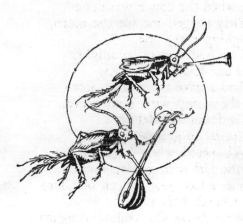

Dancing for a Prize

Three fairies by the Sangamon
   Were dancing for a prize.
The rascals were alike indeed
   As they danced with drooping eyes.
I gave the magic acorn
   To the one I loved the best,
The imp that made me think of her
   My heart's eternal guest,
My lady of the tea-rose, my lady far away,
   Queen of the fleets of No-Man's-Land
That sail to old Cathay.
   How did the trifler hint of her?
Ah, when the dance was done
   They begged me for the acorn,
Laughing every one.
   Two had eyes of midnight,
And one had golden eyes,
   And I gave the golden acorn
To the scamp with golden eyes.
   Confessor Dandelion,
My priest so gray and wise,
   Whispered when I gave it
To the girl with golden eyes:
  "She is like your Queen of Glory
On China's holy strand
   Who drove the coiling dragons
Like doves before her hand."

The King of Yellow Butterflies

(A Poem Game)

The King of Yellow Butterflies,
The King of Yellow Butterflies,
The King of Yellow Butterflies,
Now orders forth his men.
He says "The time is almost here
When violets bloom again."
Adown the road the fickle rout
Goes flashing proud and bold,
Adown the road the fickle rout
Goes flashing proud and bold,
Adown the road the fickle rout
Goes flashing proud and bold,
They shiver by the shallow pools,
They shiver by the shallow pools,
They shiver by the shallow pools,
And whimper of the cold.
They drink and drink. A frail pretense!
They love to pose and preen.
Each pool is but a looking-glass,
Where their sweet wings are seen.
Each pool is but a looking-glass,
Where their sweet wings are seen.
Each pool is but a looking-glass,
Where their sweet wings are seen.
Gentlemen adventurers! Gypsies every whit!
They live on what they steal. Their wings
By briars are frayed a bit.
Their loves are light. They have no house.
And if it rains today,
They'll climb into your cattle-shed,

They'll climb into your cattle-shed,
They'll climb into your cattle-shed,
And hide them in the hay,
And hide them in the hay,
And hide them in the hay,
And hide them in the hay.

The Potatoes' Dance

(A Poem Game)

I

"Down cellar," said the cricket,
"Down cellar," said the cricket,
"Down cellar," said the cricket,
"I saw a ball last night,
In honor of a lady,
In honor of a lady,
In honor of a lady,
Whose wings were pearly white.
The breath of bitter weather,
The breath of bitter weather,
The breath of bitter weather,
Had smashed the cellar pane.
We entertained a drift of leaves,
We entertained a drift of leaves,
We entertained a drift of leaves,
And then of snow and rain.
But we were dressed for winter,
But we were dressed for winter,
But we were dressed for winter,
And loved to hear it blow
In honor of the lady,
In honor of the lady,
In honor of the lady,
Who makes potatoes grow,
Our guest the Irish lady,
The tiny Irish lady,
The airy Irish lady,
Who makes potatoes grow.

II

"Potatoes were the waiters,
Potatoes were the waiters,
Potatoes were the waiters,
Potatoes were the band,
Potatoes were the dancers
Kicking up the sand,
Kicking up the sand,
Kicking up the sand,
Potatoes were the dancers
Kicking up the sand.
Their legs were old burnt matches,
Their legs were old burnt matches,
Their legs were old burnt matches,
Their arms were just the same.
They jigged and whirled and scrambled,
Jigged and whirled and scrambled,
Jigged and whirled and scrambled,
In honor of the dame,
The noble Irish lady
Who makes potatoes dance,
The witty Irish lady,
The saucy Irish lady,
The laughing Irish lady
Who makes potatoes prance.

III

"There was just one sweet potato.
He was golden brown and slim.
The lady loved his dancing,
The lady loved his dancing,
The lady loved his dancing,
She danced all night with him,
She danced all night with him.
Alas, he wasn't Irish.
So when she flew away,
They threw him in the coal-bin,
And there he is today,
Where they cannot hear his sighs
And his weeping for the lady,
The glorious Irish lady,
The beauteous Irish lady,
Who
Gives
Potatoes
Eyes."

The Sea Serpent Chantey

I

There's a snake on the western wave
And his crest is red.
He is long as a city street,
And he eats the dead.
There's a hole in the bottom of the sea
Where the snake goes down.
And he waits in the bottom of the sea
For the men that drown.
    Chorus:—
  This is the voice of the sand
  (The sailors understand)
  "There is far more sea than sand,
  There is far more sea than land.
    Yo . . . ho, yo . . . ho."

*Let the audi-
ence join in
the chorus.*

34

II

He waits by the door of his cave
While the ages moan.
He cracks the ribs of the ships
With his teeth of stone.
In his gizzard deep and long
Much treasure lies.
Oh, the pearls and the Spanish gold. . . .
And the idols' eyes. . . .
Oh, the totem poles . . . the skulls . . .
The altars cold . . .
The wedding rings, the dice . . .
The buoy bells old.
    Chorus:—This is the voice, etc.

III

Dive, mermaids, with sharp swords
And cut him through,
And bring us the idols' eyes
And the red gold too.
Lower the grappling hooks
Good pirate men
And drag him up by the tongue
From his deep wet den.
We will sail to the end of the world, *Repeat as a*
We will nail his hide   *second chorus*
To the mainmast of the moon   *many times.*
In the evening tide.

IV

Or will you let him live,
The deep-sea thing,
With the wrecks of all the world
In a black wide ring
By the hole in the bottom of the sea
Where the snake goes down,
Where he waits in the bottom of the sea
For the men that drown?
    Chorus:—This is the voice, etc.

An Indian Summer Day on the Prairie

In the Beginning

The sun is a huntress young,
The sun is a red, red joy,
The sun is an Indian girl,
Of the tribe of the Illinois.

Mid-Morning

The sun is a smoldering fire,
That creeps through the high gray plain,
And leaves not a bush of cloud
To blossom with flowers of rain.

Noon

The sun is a wounded deer,
That treads pale grass in the skies,
Shaking his golden horns,
Flashing his baleful eyes.

Sunset

The sun is an eagle old,
There in the windless west.
Atop of the spirit-cliffs
He builds him a crimson nest.

PART II
MOON POEMS

The Haughty Snail-King

(What Uncle William Told the Children)

Twelve snails went walking after night.
They'd creep an inch or so,
Then stop and bug their eyes
And blow.
Some folks . . . are . . . deadly . . . slow.
Twelve snails went walking yestereve,
Led by their fat old king.
They were so dull their princeling had
No sceptre, robe or ring—
Only a paper cap to wear
When nightly journeying.

This king-snail said: "I feel a thought
Within . . . It blossoms soon. . . .
O little courtiers of mine, . . .
I crave a pretty boon. . . .
Oh, yes . . . (High thoughts with effort come
And well-bred snails are ALMOST dumb.)
"I wish I had a yellow crown
As glistering . . . as . . . the moon."

The Moon's the North Wind's Cooky

(What the Little Girl Said)

The Moon's the North Wind's cooky.
He bites it, day by day,
Until there's but a rim of scraps
That crumble all away.

The South Wind is a baker.
He kneads clouds in his den,
And bakes a crisp new moon *that . . . greedy
North . . . Wind . . . eats . . . again!*

What the Rattlesnake Said

The moon's a little prairie-dog.
He shivers through the night.
He sits upon his hill and cries
For fear that *I* will bite.

The sun's a broncho. He's afraid
Like every other thing,
And trembles, morning, noon and night,
Lest *I* should spring, and sting.

Yet Gentle Will the Griffin Be

(What Grandpa Told the Children)

The moon? It is a griffin's egg,
Hatching to-morrow night.
And how the little boys will watch
With shouting and delight
To see him break the shell and stretch
And creep across the sky.
The boys will laugh. The little girls,
I fear, may hide and cry.
Yet gentle will the griffin be,
Most decorous and fat,
And walk up to the Milky Way
And lap it like a cat.

Drying Their Wings

(What the Carpenter Said)

The moon's a cottage with a door.
Some folks can see it plain.
Look, you may catch a glint of light,
A sparkle through the pane,
Showing the place is brighter still
Within, though bright without.
There, at a cosy open fire
Strange babes are grouped about.
The children of the wind and tide—
The urchins of the sky,
Drying their wings from storms and things
So they again can fly.

What the Clown Said

"The moon's a paper jumping hoop,"
 Went on the circus clown,
"A film of gilded nonsense
 For the games of Angel-town.

"If I could break those horses
 That gallop through my sleep,
I'd reach that aggravating hoop
 And make my finest leap.

"I climb upon their backs, and ride,
 But always slip too soon . . .
And fall and wake, when just one mile
 Remains to reach the moon."

The Old Horse in the City

The moon's a peck of corn.   It lies
Heaped up for me to eat.
I wish that I might climb the path
And taste that supper sweet.

Men feed me straw and scanty grain
And beat me till I'm sore.
Some day I'll break the halter-rope
And smash the stable-door,

Run down the street and mount the hill
Just as the corn appears.
I've seen it rise at certain times
For years and years and years.

The Path in the Sky

I sailed a little shallop
Upon a pretty sea
In blue and hazy mountains,
Scarce mountains unto me;
Their summits lost in wonder,
They wrapped the lake around,
And when my shallop landed
I trod on a vague ground,

And climbed and climbed toward heaven,
Though scarce before my feet
I found one step unveiled there
The blue-haze vast, complete,
Until I came to Zion
The gravel paths of God,
My endless trail pierced the thick veil
To flaming flowers and sod.
I rested, looked behind me
And saw where I had been.
My little lake. It was the moon.
Sky-mountains closed it in.

What the Snow Man Said

The Moon's a snowball. See the drifts
Of white that cross the sphere.
The Moon's a snowball, melted down
A dozen times a year.

Yet rolled again in hot July
When all my days are done
And cool to greet the weary eye
After the scorching sun.

The Moon's a piece of winter fair
Renewed the year around,
Behold it, deathless and unstained,
Above the grimy ground!

It rolls on high so brave and white
Where the clear air-rivers flow,
Proclaiming Christmas all the time
And the glory of the snow!

What the Scarecrow Said

The dim-winged spirits of the night
Do fear and serve me well.
They creep from out the hedges of
The garden where I dwell.

I wave my arms across the walk.
The troops obey the sign,
And bring me shimmering shadow-robes
And cups of cowslip-wine.

Then dig a treasure called the moon,
A very precious thing,
And keep it in the air for me
Because I am a King.

What Grandpa Mouse Said

The moon's a holy owl-queen.
She keeps them in a jar
Under her arm till evening,
Then sallies forth to war.

She pours the owls upon us.
They hoot with horrid noise
And eat the naughty mousie-girls
And wicked mousie-boys.

So climb the moonvine every night
And to the owl-queen pray:
Leave good green cheese by moonlit trees
For her to take away.

What the Forester Said

The moon is but a candle-glow
That flickers thro' the gloom:
The starry space, a castle hall:
And Earth, the children's room,
Where all night long the old trees stand
To watch the streams asleep:
Grandmothers guarding trundle-beds:
Good shepherds guarding sheep.

On the Garden Wall

Oh, once I walked a garden
In dreams.   'Twas yellow grass.
And many orange-trees grew there
In sand as white as glass.
The curving, wide wall-border
Was marble, like the snow.
I walked that wall a fairy prince
And, pacing quaint and slow,
Beside me were my pages,
Two giant, friendly birds.
Half swan they were, half peacock.
They spake in courtier-words.
Their inner wings a chariot,
Their outer wings for flight,
They lifted me from dreamland.
We bade those trees good-night.
Swiftly above the stars we rode.
I looked below me soon.
The white-walled garden I had ruled
Was one lone flower—the moon.

What the Gray-Winged Fairy Said

The moon's a gong, hung in the wild,
Whose song the fays hold dear.
Of course you do not hear it, child.
It takes a FAIRY ear.

The full moon is a splendid gong
That beats as night grows still.
It sounds above the evening song
Of dove or whippoorwill.

A Net to Snare the Moonlight

(What the Man of Faith Said)

The dew, the rain and moonlight
All prove our Father's mind.
The dew, the rain and moonlight
Descend to bless mankind.

Come, let us see that all men
Have land to catch the rain,
Have grass to snare the spheres of dew,
And fields spread for the grain.

Yea, we would give to each poor man
Ripe wheat and poppies red,
A peaceful place at evening
With the stars just overhead:

A net to snare the moonlight,
A sod spread to the sun,
A place of toil by daytime,
Of dreams when toil is done.

PART III

STORIES AND HEROES

The Ghost of the Buffaloes

Last night at black midnight I woke with a cry,
The windows were shaking, there was thunder on high,
The floor was atremble, the door was ajar,
White fires, crimson fires, shone from afar.
I rushed to the dooryard.   The city was gone.
My home was a hut without orchard or lawn.
It was mud-smear and logs near a whispering stream,
Nothing else built by man could I see in my dream . . .
Then . . .
Ghost-kings came headlong, row upon row,
Gods of the Indians, torches aglow.

They mounted the bear and the elk and the deer,
And eagles gigantic, aged and sere,
They rode long-horn cattle, they cried "A-la-la."
They lifted the knife, the bow, and the spear,
They lifted ghost-torches from dead fires below,
The midnight made grand with the cry "A-la-la."
The midnight made grand with a red-god charge,
A red-god show,
A red-god show,
"A-la-la, a-la-la, a-la-la, a-la-la."

With bodies like bronze, and terrible eyes
Came the rank and the file, with catamount cries,
Gibbering, yipping, with hollow-skull clacks,
Riding white bronchos with skeleton backs,
Scalp-hunters, beaded and spangled and bad,
Naked and lustful and foaming and mad,
Flashing primeval demoniac scorn,
Blood-thirst and pomp amid darkness reborn,
Power and glory that sleep in the grass
While the winds and the snows and the great rains pass.

They crossed the gray river, thousands abreast,
They rode in infinite lines to the west,
Tide upon tide of strange fury and foam,
Spirits and wraiths, the blue was their home,
The sky was their goal where the star-flags were furled,
And on past those far golden splendors they whirled.
They burned to dim meteors, lost in the deep,
And I turned in dazed wonder, thinking of sleep.

And the wind crept by
Alone, unkempt, unsatisfied,
The wind cried and cried—
Muttered of massacres long past,
Buffaloes in shambles vast . . .
An owl said: "Hark, what is a-wing?"
I heard a cricket carolling,
I heard a cricket carolling,
I heard a cricket carolling.

Then . . .
Snuffing the lightning that crashed from on high
Rose royal old buffaloes, row upon row.
The lords of the prairie came galloping by.
And I cried in my heart "A-la-la, a-la-la,
A red-god show,
A red-god show,
A-la-la, a-la-la, a-la-la, a-la-la."

Buffaloes, buffaloes; thousands abreast,
A scourge and amazement, they swept to the west.
With black bobbing noses, with red rolling tongues,
Coughing forth steam from their leather-wrapped lungs,
Cows with their calves, bulls big and vain,
Goring the laggards, shaking the mane,
Stamping flint feet, flashing moon eyes.
Pompous and owlish, shaggy and wise.

Like sea-cliffs and caves resounded their ranks
With shoulders like waves, and undulant flanks.
Tide upon tide of strange fury and foam,
Spirits and wraiths, the blue was their home,
The sky was their goal where the star-flags are furled,
And on past those far golden splendors they whirled.
They burned to dim meteors, lost in the deep,
And I turned in dazed wonder, thinking of sleep.

I heard a cricket's cymbals play,
A scarecrow lightly flapped his rags,
And a pan that hung by his shoulder rang,
Rattled and thumped in a listless way,
And now the wind in the chimney sang,
The wind in the chimney,
The wind in the chimney,
The wind in the chimney,
    Seemed to say:—
"Dream, boy, dream,
If you anywise can.
To dream is the work
Of beast or man.
Life is the west-going dream-storms' breath,
Life is a dream, the sigh of the skies,
The breath of the stars, that nod on their pillows
With their golden hair mussed over their eyes."

The locust played on his musical wing,
Sang to his mate of love's delight.
I heard the whippoorwill's soft fret.
I heard a cricket carolling,
I heard a cricket carolling,
I heard a cricket say: "Good-night, good-night,
Good-night, good-night, . . . good-night."

The Broncho That Would Not Be Broken

A little colt—broncho, loaned to the farm
To be broken in time without fury or harm,
Yet black crows flew past you, shouting alarm,
Calling "Beware," with lugubrious singing . . .
The butterflies there in the bush were romancing,
The smell of the grass caught your soul in a trance,
So why be a-fearing the spurs and the traces,
O broncho that would not be broken of dancing?

You were born with the pride of the lords great and olden
Who danced, through the ages, in corridors golden.
In all the wide farm-place the person most human.
You spoke out so plainly with squealing and capering,
With whinnying, snorting, contorting and prancing,
As you dodged your pursuers, looking askance,
With Greek-footed figures, and Parthenon paces,
O broncho that would not be broken of dancing.

The grasshoppers cheered. "Keep whirling," they said.
The insolent sparrows called from the shed
"If men will not laugh, make them wish they were dead."
But arch were your thoughts, all malice displacing,
Though the horse-killers came, with snake-whips
     advancing.
You bantered and cantered away your last chance.
And they scourged you, with Hell in their speech and
     their faces,
O broncho that would not be broken of dancing.

"Nobody cares for you," rattled the crows,
As you dragged the whole reaper, next day, down the
    rows.
The three mules held back, yet you danced on your toes.
You pulled like a racer, and kept the mules chasing.
You tangled the harness with bright eyes side-glancing,
While the drunk driver bled you—a pole for a lance—
And the giant mules bit at you—keeping their places.
O broncho that would not be broken of dancing.

In that last afternoon your boyish heart broke.
The hot wind came down like a sledge-hammer stroke.
The blood-sucking flies to a rare feast awoke.
And they searched out your wounds, your death-warrant
    tracing.
And the merciful men, their religion enhancing,
Stopped the red reaper, to give you a chance.
Then you died on the prairie, and scorned all disgraces,
O broncho that would not be broken of dancing.

SOUVENIR OF GREAT BEND, KANSAS.

In Praise of Johnny Appleseed *

(Born 1775; died 1847)

I. OVER THE APPALACHIAN BARRICADE

In the days of President Washington,
The glory of the nations,
Dust and ashes,
Snow and sleet,
And hay and oats and wheat,
Blew west,
Crossed the Appalachians,
Found the glades of rotting leaves, the soft deer-pastures,
The farms of the far-off future
In the forest.
Colts jumped the fence,

*To be read
like old leaves
on the elm
tree of Time,
Sifting soft
winds with
sentence and
rhyme.*

* The best account of John Chapman's career, under the name "Johnny Appleseed," is to be found in *Harper's Monthly Magazine*, November, 1871.

Snorting, ramping, snapping, sniffing,
With gastronomic calculations,
Crossed the Appalachians,
The east walls of our citadel,
And turned to gold-horned unicorns,
Feasting in the dim, volunteer farms of the forest.
Stripedest, kickingest kittens escaped,
Caterwauling "Yankee Doodle Dandy."
Renounced their poor relations,
Crossed the Appalachians,
And turned to tiny tigers
In the humorous forest.
Chickens escaped
From farmyard congregations,
Crossed the Appalachians,
And turned to amber trumpets
On the ramparts of our Hoosiers' nest and citadel,
Millennial heralds
Of the foggy mazy forest.
Pigs broke loose, scrambled west,
Scorned their loathsome stations,
Crossed the Appalachians,
Turned to roaming, foaming wild boars
Of the forest.
The smallest, blindest puppies toddled west
While their eyes were coming open,
And, with misty observations,
Crossed the Appalachians,
Barked, barked, barked
At the glow-worms and the marsh lights and the light-
      ning-bugs,
And turned to ravening wolves
Of the forest.
Crazy parrots and canaries flew west,

Drunk on May-time revelations,
Crossed the Appalachians,
And turned to delirious, flower-dressed fairies
Of the lazy forest.
Haughtiest swans and peacocks swept west,
And, despite soft derivations,
Crossed the Appalachians.
And turned to blazing warrior souls
Of the forest,
Singing the ways
Of the Ancient of Days.
And the "Old Continentals
In their ragged regimentals,"
With bard's imaginations,
Crossed the Appalachians.
And
A boy
Blew west,
And with prayers and incantations,
And with "Yankee Doodle Dandy,"
Crossed the Appalachians,
And was "young John Chapman,"
Then
"Johnny Appleseed, Johnny Appleseed,"
Chief of the fastnesses, dappled and vast,
In a pack on his back,
In a deer-hide sack,
The beautiful orchards of the past,
The ghosts of all the forests and the groves—
In that pack on his back,
In that talisman sack,
To-morrow's peaches, pears, and cherries,
To-morrow's grapes and red raspberries,
Seeds and tree-souls, precious things,

Feathered with microscopic wings,
All the outdoors the child heart knows,
And the apple, green, red, and white,
Sun of his day and his night—
The apple allied to the thorn,
Child of the rose.
Porches untrod of forest houses
All before him, all day long,
"Yankee Doodle" his marching song;
And the evening breeze
Joined his psalms of praise
As he sang the ways
Of the Ancient of Days.
Leaving behind august Virginia,
Proud Massachusetts, and proud Maine.
Planting the trees that would march and train
On, in his name to the great Pacific,
Like Birnam wood to Dunsinane,
Johnny Appleseed swept on,
Every shackle gone,
Loving every sloshy brake,
Loving every skunk and snake,
Loving every leathery weed,
Johnny Appleseed, Johnny Appleseed,
Master and ruler of the unicorn-ramping forest,
The tiger-mewing forest,
The rooster-trumpeting, boar-foaming, wolf-ravening
    forest,
The spirit-haunted, fairy-enchanted forest,
Stupendous and endless,
Searching its perilous ways
In the name of the Ancient of Days.

II. The Indians Worship Him, but He Hurries On

Painted kings in the midst of the clearing
Heard him asking his friends the eagles
To guard each planted seed and seedling.
Then he was a god, to the red man's dreaming;
Then the chiefs brought treasures grotesque and fair,—
Magical trinkets and pipes and guns,
Beads and furs from their medicine-lair,—
Stuck holy feathers in his hair.
Hailed him with austere delight.
The orchard god was their guest through the night.

While the late snow blew from bleak Lake Erie,
Scourging rock and river and reed,
All night long they made great medicine
For Jonathan Chapman,
Johnny Appleseed,
Johnny Appleseed;
And as though his heart were a wind-blown wheat
    sheaf,

As though his heart were a new built nest,
As though their heaven house were his breast,
In swept the snowbirds singing glory.
And I hear his bird heart beat its story,
Hear yet how the ghost of the forest shivers,
Hear yet the cry of the gray, old orchards,
Dim and decaying by the rivers,
And the timid wings of the bird-ghosts beating,
And the ghosts of the tom-toms beating, beating.

But he left their wigwams and their love.   *While you*
By the hour of dawn he was proud and stark,   *read, hear*
Kissed the Indian babes with a sigh,   *the hoof-*
                                                beats of deer
Went forth to live on roots and bark,   *in the snow.*
Sleep in the trees, while the years howled by. *And see, by*
                                                their track,
Calling the catamounts by name,   *bleeding*
And buffalo bulls no hand could tame.   *footprints*
Slaying never a living creature,   *we know.*
Joining the birds in every game,
With the gorgeous turkey gobblers mocking,
With the lean-necked eagles boxing and shouting;
Sticking their feathers in his hair,—
Turkey feathers,
Eagle feathers,
Trading hearts with all beasts and weathers
He swept on, winged and wonder-crested,
Bare-armed, barefooted, and bare-breasted.
The maples, shedding their spinning seeds,   *While you*
                                                 read, see
Called to his appleseeds in the ground,   *conventions of*
Vast chestnut-trees, with their butterfly nations, *deer go by.*
Called to his seeds without a sound.   *The bucks*
                                                 toss their
And the chipmunk turned a "summerset."   *horns, the*
And the foxes danced the Virginia reel;   *fuzzy fawns*
                                                 fly.
Hawthorn and crab-thorn bent, rain-wet,

And dropped their flowers in his night-black hair;
And the soft fawns stopped for his perorations;
And his black eyes shone through the forest-gleam,
And he plunged young hands into new-turned earth,
And prayed dear orchard boughs into birth;
And he ran with the rabbit and slept with the stream,
And he ran with the rabbit and slept with the stream,
And he ran with the rabbit and slept with the stream.
And so for us he made great medicine,
And so for us he made great medicine,
And so for us he made great medicine.
In the days of President Washington.

III. Johnny Appleseed's Old Age

Long, long after,
When settlers put up beam and rafter,
They asked of the birds: "Who gave this fruit?
Who watched this fence till the seeds took root?
Who gave these boughs?" They asked the sky,
And there was no reply.
But the robin might have said,
"To the farthest West he has followed the
    sun,
His life and his empire just begun."
Self-scourged, like a monk, with a throne
    for wages,
Stripped, like the iron-souled Hindu sages,
Draped like a statue, in strings like a scare-
    crow,
His helmet-hat an old tin pan,
But worn in the love of the heart of man,
More sane than the helm of Tamerlane!

To be read like faint hoof-beats of fawns long gone From respectable pasture, and park and lawn, And heart-beats of fawns that are coming again When the forest, once more, is the master of men.

89

Hairy Ainu, wild man of Borneo, Robinson Crusoe—
    Johnny Appleseed!
And the robin might have said,
"Sowing, he goes to the far, new West,
With the apple, the sun of his burning breast—
The apple allied to the thorn,
Child of the rose."

Washington buried in Virginia,
Jackson buried in Tennessee,
Young Lincoln, brooding in Illinois,
And Johnny Appleseed, priestly and free,
Knotted and gnarled, past seventy years,
Still planted on in the woods alone.
Ohio and young Indiana—
These were his wide altar-stone,
Where still he burnt out flesh and bone.
Twenty days ahead of the Indian, twenty years ahead of
    the white man,
At last the Indian overtook him, at last the Indian
    hurried past him;
At last the white man overtook him, at last the white man
    hurried past him;
At last his own trees overtook him, at last his own trees
    hurried past him.
Many cats were tame again,
Many ponies tame again,
Many pigs were tame again,
Many canaries tame again;
And the real frontier was his sunburnt breast.
From the fiery core of that apple, the earth,
Sprang apple-amaranths divine.
Love's orchards climbed to the heavens of the West
And snowed the earthly sod with flowers.

Farm hands from the terraces of the blest
Danced on the mists with their ladies fine;
And Johnny Appleseed laughed with his dreams,
And swam once more the ice-cold streams.
And the doves of the spirit swept through the hours,
With doom-calls, love-calls, death-calls, dream-calls;
And Johnny Appleseed, all that year,
Lifted his hands to the farm-filled sky,
To the apple-harvesters busy on high;
And so once more his youth began,
And so for us he made great medicine—
Johnny Appleseed, medicine-man.
Then
The sun was their turned-up broken barrel,
Out of which their juicy apples rolled,
Down the repeated terraces,
Thumping across the gold,
An angel in each apple that touched the forest mold,
A ballot-box in each apple,
A state capital in each apple,
Great high schools, great colleges,
All America in each apple,
Each red, rich, round, and bouncing moon
That touched the forest mold.
Like scrolls and rolled-up flags of silk,
He saw the fruits unfold,
And all our expectations in one wild-flower written
     dream.
Confusion, and death-sweetness, and a thicket of crab-
     thorns!
Heart of a hundred midnights, heart of the merciful
     morns.
Heaven's boughs bent down with their alchemy,
Perfumed airs, and thoughts of wonder.

And the dew on the grass and his own cold tears
Were one in brooding mystery,
Though death's loud thunder came upon him,
Though death's loud thunder struck him down—
The boughs and the proud thoughts swept through the
    thunder,
Till he saw our wide nation, each State a flower,
Each petal a park for holy feet,
With wild fawns merry on every street,
With wild fawns merry on every street,
The vista of ten thousand years, flower-lighted and
    complete.

Hear the lazy weeds murmuring, bays and rivers whisper-
    ing,
From Michigan to Texas, California to Maine;
Listen to the eagles screaming, calling,
"Johnny Appleseed, Johnny Appleseed,"
There by the doors of old Fort Wayne.

In the four-poster bed Johnny Appleseed built,
Autumn rains were the curtains, autumn leaves were the
    quilt.
He laid him down sweetly, and slept through the night,
Like a stone washed white,
There by the doors of old Fort Wayne.

The Congo *

A Study of the Negro Race

(Being a memorial to Ray Eldred, a Disciple missionary
of the Congo River)

I. Their Basic Savagery

Fat black bucks in a wine-barrel room,
Barrel-house kings, with feet unstable,
Sagged and reeled and pounded on the   *A deep rolling*
    table,   *bass.*
Pounded on the table,
Beat an empty barrel with the handle of a broom,
Hard as they were able,
Boom, boom, Boom,
With a silk umbrella and the handle of a broom,
Boomlay, boomlay, boomlay, Boom.
Then I had religion, Then I had a vision.
I could not turn from their revel in derision.

*This poem, particularly the third section, was suggested by an
allusion in a sermon by my pastor, F. W. Burnham, to the heroic
life and death of Ray Eldred. Eldred was a missionary of the
Disciples of Christ who perished while swimming a treacherous
branch of the Congo. See *A Master Builder on the Congo*, by
Andrew F. Henesey, published by Fleming H. Revell.

THEN I SAW THE CONGO, CREEPING
    THROUGH THE BLACK,
CUTTING THROUGH THE FOREST WITH A
    GOLDEN TRACK.

More deliberate.
Solemnly
chanted.

Then along that riverbank
A thousand miles
Tattooed cannibals danced in files;
Then I heard the boom of the blood-lust song
And a thigh-bone beating on a tin-pan
    gong.

A rapidly
piling climax
of speed and
racket.

And "BLOOD" screamed the whistles and
    the fifes of the warriors,
"BLOOD" screamed the skull-faced, lean witch-
    doctors,
"Whirl ye the deadly voo-doo rattle,
Harry the uplands,
Steal all the cattle,
Rattle-rattle, rattle-rattle,
Bing.
Boomlay, boomlay, boomlay, BOOM,"
A roaring, epic, rag-time tune

With a philo-
sophic pause.

From the mouth of the Congo
To the Mountains of the Moon.
Death is an Elephant,
Torch-eyed and horrible,
Foam-flanked and terrible.

Shrilly and
with a heavily
accented metre.

BOOM, steal the pygmies,
BOOM, kill the Arabs,
BOOM, kill the white men,
Hoo, Hoo, Hoo.
Listen to the yell of Leopold's ghost
Burning in Hell for his hand-maimed host.

Like the wind
in the chimney.

Hear how the demons chuckle and yell
Cutting his hands off, down in Hell.
Listen to the creepy proclamation,
Blown through the lairs of the forest-nation,
Blown past the white-ants' hill of clay,
Blown past the marsh where the butterflies
     play:—
"Be careful what you do,
Or Mumbo-Jumbo, God of the Congo,
And all of the other
Gods of the Congo,
Mumbo-Jumbo will hoo-doo you,
Mumbo-Jumbo will hoo-doo you,
Mumbo-Jumbo will hoo-doo you."

*All the "o"
sounds very
golden. Heavy
accents very
heavy. Light
accents very
light. Last line
whispered.*

II. THEIR IRREPRESSIBLE HIGH SPIRITS

Wild crap-shooters with a whoop and a call   *Rather shrill*
Danced the juba in their gambling hall   *and high.*
And laughed fit to kill, and shook the town,
And guyed the policemen and laughed them down
With a boomlay, boomlay, boomlay, BOOM.
THEN I SAW THE CONGO, CREEPING   *Read exactly as*
    THROUGH THE BLACK,   *in first section.*
CUTTING THROUGH THE FOREST WITH A
    GOLDEN TRACK.
A Negro fairyland swung into view,   *Lay emphasis*
A minstrel river   *on the delicate*
                                            ideas. Keep as
Where dreams come true.   *light-footed as*
The ebony palace soared on high   *possible.*
Through the blossoming trees to the evening sky.
The inlaid porches and casements shone
With gold and ivory and elephant-bone.
And the black crowd laughed till their sides were sore
At the baboon butler in the agate door,
And the well-known tunes of the parrot band
That trilled on the bushes of that magic land.

A troupe of skull-faced witch-men came   *With*
Through the agate doorway in suits of flame,   *pomposity.*
Yea, long-tailed coats with a gold-leaf crust
And hats that were covered with diamond-dust.
And the crowd in the court gave a whoop and a call
And danced the juba from wall to wall.

But the witch-men suddenly stilled the
    throng

*With a great
deliberation
and ghostliness.*

With a stern cold glare, and a stern old
    song:—

"Mumbo-Jumbo will hoo-doo you." . . .

Just then from the doorway, as fat as
    shotes,

*With over-
whelming as-
surance, good
cheer, and
pomp.*

Came the cake-walk princes in their long
    red coats,

Canes with a brilliant lacquer shine,

And tall silk hats that were red as wine.

And they pranced with their butterfly
    partners there,

*With growing
speed and
sharply marked
dance-rhythm.*

Coal-black maidens with pearls in their
    hair,

Knee-skirts trimmed with the jassamine sweet,

And bells on their ankles and little black feet.

And the couples railed at the chant and the frown

Of the witch-men lean, and laughed them down.

(Oh, rare was the revel, and well worth while

That made those glowering witch-men smile.)

The cake-walk royalty then began

To walk for a cake that was tall as a man

To the tune of "Boomlay, boomlay, Boom,"

While the witch-men laughed, with a
    sinister air,

*With a touch
of Negro dia-
lect, and
as rapidly as
possible toward
the end.*

And sang with the scalawags prancing
    there:—

"Walk with care, walk with care,
Or Mumbo-Jumbo, God of the Congo,
And all of the other Gods of the Congo,
Mumbo-Jumbo will hoo-doo you.
Beware, beware, walk with care,
Boomlay, boomlay, boomlay, boom.
Boomlay, boomlay, boomlay, boom.
Boomlay, boomlay, boomlay, boom.
Boomlay, boomlay, boomlay,
Boom."
(Oh, rare was the revel, and well worth *Slow philo-*
    while   *sophic calm.*
That made those glowering witch-men smile.)

III. The Hope of Their Religion

A good old Negro in the slums of the town
Preached at a sister for her velvet gown.
Howled at a brother for his low-down
    ways,
His prowling, guzzling, sneak-thief days.
Beat on the Bible till he wore it out
Starting the jubilee revival shout.
And some had visions, as they stood on chairs,
And sang of Jacob, and the golden stairs,
And they all repented, a thousand strong
From their stupor and savagery and sin and wrong
And slammed with their hymn books till they shook
    the room
With "glory, glory, glory,"
And "Boom, boom, Boom."
THEN I SAW THE CONGO, CREEPING
    THROUGH THE BLACK,
CUTTING THROUGH THE JUNGLE WITH
    A GOLDEN TRACK.
And the gray sky opened like a new-rent veil
And showed the Apostles with their coats of mail.
In bright white steel they were seated round
And their fire-eyes watched where the Congo wound.
And the twelve Apostles, from their thrones on high
Thrilled all the forest with their heavenly cry:—
"Mumbo-Jumbo will die in the jungle;
Never again will he hoo-doo you,
Never again will he hoo-doo you."

*Heavy bass.
With a literal
imitation of
camp-meeting
racket, and
trance.*

*Exactly as in
the first section.
Begin with
terror and
power, end with
joy.*

*Sung to the
tune of "Hark,
ten thousand
harps and
voices."*

99

Then along that river, a thousand miles
The vine-snared trees fell down in files.

With growing deliberation and joy.

Pioneer angels cleared the way
For a Congo paradise, for babes at play,
For sacred capitals, for temples clean.
Gone were the skull-faced witch-men lean.
There, where the wild ghost-gods had
    wailed

In a rather high key—as delicately as possible.

A million boats of the angels sailed
With oars of silver, and prows of blue
And silken pennants that the sun shone through.
'Twas a land transfigured, 'twas a new creation.
Oh, a singing wind swept the Negro nation
And on through the backwoods clearing flew:—
"Mumbo-Jumbo is dead in the jungle.

To the tune of "Hark, ten thousand harps and voices."

Never again will he hoo-doo you.
Never again will he hoo-doo you."

Redeemed were the forests, the beasts and the men,
And only the vulture dared again
By the far, lone mountains of the moon
To cry, in the silence, the Congo tune:—
"Mumbo-Jumbo will hoo-doo you,

Dying down into a pene-trating, terrified whisper.

Mumbo-Jumbo will hoo-doo you.
Mumbo . . . Jumbo . . . will . . . hoo-doo
    . . . you."

Abraham Lincoln Walks at Midnight

(In Springfield, Illinois)

It is portentous, and a thing of state
That here at midnight, in our little town
A mourning figure walks, and will not rest,
Near the old court-house pacing up and down,

Or by his homestead, or in shadowed yards
He lingers where his children used to play,
Or through the market, on the well-worn stones
He stalks until the dawn-stars burn away.

A bronzed, lank man! His suit of ancient black,
A famous high top-hat and plain worn shawl
Make him the quaint great figure that men love,
The prairie-lawyer, master of us all.

He cannot sleep upon his hillside now.
He is among us:—as in times before!
And we who toss and lie awake for long
Breathe deep, and start, to see him pass the door.

His head is bowed. He thinks on men and kings.
Yea, when the sick world cries, how can he sleep?
Too many peasants fight, they know not why,
Too many homesteads in black terror weep.

The sins of all the war-lords burn his heart.
He sees the dreadnaughts scouring every main.
He carries on his shawl-wrapped shoulders now
The bitterness, the folly and the pain.

He cannot rest until a spirit-dawn
Shall come;—the shining hope of Europe free:
The league of sober folk, the Workers' Earth,
Bringing long peace to Cornland, Alp and Sea.

It breaks his heart that kings must murder still,
That all his hours of travail here for men
Seem yet in vain.   And who will bring white peace
That he may sleep upon his hill again?

From the Litany of the Heroes

Would that we had the fortunes of Columbus.
Sailing his caravels a trackless way,
He found a Universe—he sought Cathay.
God give such dawns as when, his venture o'er,
The Sailor looked upon San Salvador.
God lead us past the setting of the sun
To wizard islands, of august surprise;
God make our blunders wise.

Would I might wake St. Francis in you
 all,
Brother of birds and trees, God's
 Troubadour,
Blinded with weeping for the sad and poor;
Our wealth undone, all strict Franciscan men,
Come, let us chant the canticle again
Of mother earth and the enduring sun.
God make each soul the lonely leper's slave;
God make us saints, and brave.

Would I might wake in you the whirlwind soul
Of Michelangelo, who hewed the stone
And Night and Day revealed, whose arm alone
Could draw the face of God, the titan high
Whose genius smote like lightning from the sky—
And shall he mold like dead leaves in the grave?
Nay, he is in us! Let us dare and dare.
God help us to be brave.

Would that in body and spirit Shakespeare came
Visible emperor of the deeds of Time,
With Justice still the genius of his rhyme,
Giving each man his due, each passion grace,
Impartial as the rain from Heaven's face
Or sunshine from the Heaven-enthroned sun.
Sweet Swan of Avon, come to us again.
Teach us to write, and writing, to be men.

Would I might rouse the Lincoln in you
    all,
That which is gendered in the wilder-
    ness
From lonely prairies and God's tenderness.
Imperial soul, star of a weedy stream,
Born where the ghosts of buffaloes still gleam,
Whose spirit hoof-beats storm above his grave,
Above that breast of earth and prairie-fire—
Fire that freed the slave.

Nay, I would have you grand, and still forgotten,
Hid like the stars at noon, as he who set
The Egyptian magic of man's alphabet;
Or that Egyptian, first to dream in pain
That dauntless souls cannot by death be slain—
Conquering for all men then, the fateful grave.
God keep us hid, yet vaster far than death.
God help us to be brave.

The Kallyope Yell

(To be given in the peculiar whispered manner of the University of Kansas "Jay-Hawk Yell")

I

Proud men
Eternally
Go about,
Slander me,
Call me the "Calliope,"
Sizz. . . .
Fizz. . . . .

II

I am the Gutter Dream,
Tune-maker, born of steam,
Tooting joy, tooting hope.
I am the Kallyope,
Car called the Kallyope.

Willy willy willy wah HOO!
See the flags: snow-white tent,
See the bear and elephant,
See the monkey jump the rope,
Listen to the Kallyope, Kallyope, Kallyope!
Soul of the rhinoceros
And the hippopotamus
(Listen to the lion roar!)
Jaguar, cockatoot,
Loons, owls,
Hoot, Hoot.
Listen to the lion roar,
Listen to the lion roar,
Listen to the lion R-O-A-R!
Hear the leopard cry for gore,
Willy willy willy wah HOO!
Hail the bloody Indian band,
Hail, all hail the popcorn stand,
Hail to Barnum's picture there,
People's idol everywhere,
Whoop, whoop, whoop, WHOOP!
Music of the mob am I,
Circus day's tremendous cry:—
I am the Kallyope, Kallyope, Kallyope!
Hoot toot, hoot toot, hoot toot, hoot toot,
Willy willy willy wah HOO!
Sizz, fizz. . . .

Born of mobs, born of steam,
Listen to my golden dream,
Listen to my golden dream,
Listen to my G-O-L-D-E-N D-R-E A-M!
Whoop whoop whoop whoop WHOOP!
I will blow the proud folk low,
Humanize the dour and slow,
I will shake the proud folk down,
(Listen to the lion roar!)
Popcorn crowds shall rule the town—
Willy willy willy wah HOO!
Steam shall work melodiously,
Brotherhood increase.
You'll see the world and all it holds
For fifty cents apiece.
Willy willy willy wah HOO!
Every day a circus day.

What?

Well, *almost* every day.
Nevermore the sweater's den,
Nevermore the prison pen.
Gone the war on land and sea
That aforetime troubled men.
Nations all in amity,
Happy in their plumes arrayed
In the long bright street parade,
Bands a-playing every day.

What?

Well, *almost* every day.
I am the Kallyope, Kallyope, Kallyope!
Willy willy willy wah HOO!
Hoot, toot, hoot, toot,
Whoop whoop whoop whoop,
Willy willy willy wah HOO!
Sizz, fizz. . . .

IV

Every soul
Resident
In the earth's one circus tent!
Every man a trapeze king

Then a pleased spectator there.
On the benches! In the ring!
While the neighbors gawk and stare
And the cheering rolls along.
Almost every day a race
When the merry starting gong
Rings, each chariot on the line,
Every driver fit and fine
With a steel-spring Roman grace.
Almost every day a dream,
Almost every day a dream.
Every girl,
Maid or wife,
Wild with music,
Eyes agleam
With that marvel called desire:

Actress, princess, fit for life,
Armed with honor like a knife,
Jumping thro' the hoops of fire.
(Listen to the lion roar!)
Making all the children shout
Clowns shall tumble all about,
Painted high and full of song
While the cheering rolls along,
Tho' they scream,
Tho' they rage,
Every beast in his cage,
Every beast in his den,
That aforetime troubled men.

V

I am the Kallyope, Kallyope, Kallyope,
Tooting hope, tooting hope, tooting hope,
    tooting hope;
Shaking window-pane and door
With a crashing cosmic tune,
With the war-cry of the spheres,
Rhythm of the roar of noon,
Rhythm of Niagara's roar,
Voicing planet, star and moon,
SHRIEKING of the better years.
Prophet-singers will arise,
Prophets coming after me,
Sing my song in softer guise
With more delicate surprise;
I am but the pioneer
Voice of the Democracy;
I am the gutter dream,
I am the golden dream,

Singing science, singing steam.
I will blow the proud folk down,
(Listen to the lion roar!)
I am the Kallyope, Kallyope, Kallyope,
Tooting hope, tooting hope, tooting hope,
        tooting hope,
Willy willy willy wah HOO!
Hoot toot, hoot toot, hoot toot, hoot toot,
Whoop whoop, whoop whoop,
Whoop whoop, whoop whoop,
Willy willy willy wah HOO!
Sizz. . . .
Fizz. . . .

The Santa-Fé Trail (A Humoresque)

(I asked the old Negro: "What is that bird that sings so well?" He answered: "That is the Rachel-Jane." "Hasn't it another name—lark, or thrush, or the like?" "No. Jus' Rachel-Jane.")

I. IN WHICH A RACING AUTO COMES FROM THE EAST

This is the order of the music of the morn-
    ing:—
First, from the far East comes but a croon-
    ing. *To be sung delicately, to an improvised tune.*
The crooning turns to a sunrise singing.
Hark to the *calm*-horn, *balm*-horn, *psalm*-horn.
Hark to the *faint*-horn, *quaint*-horn, *saint*-horn . . .

Hark to the *pace*-horn, *chase*-horn, *race*-
    horn. *To be sung or read with great speed.*
And the holy veil of the dawn has gone.
Swiftly the brazen car comes on.
It burns in the East as the sunrise burns.
I see great flashes where the far trail turns.
Its eyes are lamps like the eyes of dragons.
It drinks gasoline from big red flagons.
Butting through the delicate mists of the morning,
It comes like lightning, goes past roaring.
It will hail all the windmills, taunting, ringing,
Dodge the cyclones,
Count the milestones,
On through the ranges the prairie-dog tills—
Scooting past the cattle on the thousand hills. . . .

Ho for the *tear*-horn, *scare*-horn, *dare*-
    horn,
Ho for the *gay*-horn, *bark*-horn, *bay*-horn.
Ho for Kansas, land that restores us
When houses choke us, and great books bore us!
Sunrise Kansas, harvesters' Kansas,
A million men have found you before us.
A million men have found you before us.

*To be read or
sung in a roll-
ing bass, with
some delibera-
tion.*

II.   In Which Many Autos Pass Westward

I want live things in their pride to remain.
I will not kill one grasshopper vain
Though he eats a hole in my shirt like a
    door.
I let him out, give him one chance more.
Perhaps, while he gnaws my hat in his whim,
Grasshopper lyrics occur to him.

*In an even,
deliberate,
narrative
manner.*

I am a tramp by the long trail's border,
Given to squalor, rags and disorder.
I nap and amble and yawn and look,
Write fool-thoughts in my grubby book,
Recite to the children, explore at my ease,
Work when I work, beg when I please,
Give crank drawings, that make folks stare
To the half-grown boys in the sunset glare,
And get me a place to sleep in the hay
At the end of a live-and-let-live day.

I find in the stubble of the new-cut weeds
A whisper and a feasting, all one needs:
The whisper of the strawberries, white and red
Here where the new-cut weeds lie dead.

But I would not walk all alone till I die
Without some life-drunk horns going by.
And up round this apple-earth they come
Blasting the whispers of the morning dumb:—
Cars in a plain realistic row.
And fair dreams fade
When the raw horns blow.

On each snapping pennant
A big black name:—
The careering city
Whence each car came.
They tour from Memphis, Atlanta, Savannah,
Tallahassee and Texarkana.
They tour from St. Louis, Columbus, Man- *Like a train-*
    istee,   *caller in a*
                                          Union Depot.
They tour from Peoria, Davenport, Kankakee.
Cars from Concord, Niagara, Boston,
Cars from Topeka, Emporia, and Austin.
Cars from Chicago, Hannibal, Cairo.
Cars from Alton, Oswego, Toledo.
Cars from Buffalo, Kokomo, Delphi,
Cars from Lodi, Carmi, Loami.
Ho for Kansas, land that restores us
When houses choke us, and great books bore us!
While I watch the highroad
And look at the sky,
While I watch the clouds in amazing grandeur
Roll their legions without rain
Over the blistering Kansas plain—
While I sit by the milestone
And watch the sky,
The United States
Goes by.

Listen to the *iron*-horns, ripping, racking,
Listen to the *quack*-horns, slack and clack-
ing.

To be given very harshly, with a snapping explosiveness.

Way down the road, trilling like a toad,
Here comes the *dice*-horn, here comes the *vice*-horn,
Here comes the *snarl*-horn, *brawl*-horn, *lewd*-horn,
Followed by the *prude*-horn, bleak and squeaking:
(Some of them from Kansas, some of them from
    Kansas.)
Here comes the *hod*-horn, *plod*-horn, *sod*-horn,
Nevermore-to-*roam*-horn, *loam*-horn, *home*-horn.
(Some of them from Kansas, some of them from
    Kansas.)

  Far away the Rachel-Jane
  Not defeated by the horns
  Sings amid a hedge of thorns:—

To be read or sung, well-nigh in a whisper.

  "Love and life,
  Eternal youth—
  Sweet, sweet, sweet, sweet,
  Dew and glory,
  Love and truth,
  Sweet, sweet, sweet, sweet."

WHILE SMOKE-BLACK FREIGHTS ON THE
  DOUBLE-TRACKED RAILROAD,

Louder and louder, faster and faster.

DRIVEN AS THOUGH BY THE FOUL FIEND'S OX-GOAD,
SCREAMING TO THE WEST COAST, SCREAMING TO THE EAST,
CARRY OFF A HARVEST, BRING BACK A FEAST,
AND HARVESTING MACHINERY AND HARNESS FOR THE
  BEAST,
THE HAND-CARS WHIZ, AND RATTLE ON THE RAILS,
THE SUNLIGHT FLASHES ON THE TIN DINNER PAILS.

And then, in an instant, ye modern men,
Behold the procession once again,
The United States goes by!

In a rolling bass, with increasing deliberation.

123

Listen to the *iron*-horns, ripping, racking,
Listen to the *wise*-horn, desperate-to-*advise*-
    horn,
Listen to the *fast*-horn, *kill*-horn, *blast*-horn. . . .

      Far away the Rachel-Jane
      Not defeated by the horns
      Sings amid a hedge of thorns:—
      "Love and life,
      Eternal youth,
      Sweet, sweet, sweet, sweet,
      Dew and glory,
      Love and truth.
      Sweet, sweet, sweet, sweet."

The mufflers open on a score of cars
With wonderful thunder,
CRACK, CRACK, CRACK,
CRACK-CRACK, CRACK-CRACK,
CRACK, CRACK, CRACK,
Listen to the *gold*-horn . . .
Old-horn . . .
Cold-horn . . .
And all of the tunes, till the night comes down
On hay-stack, and ant-hill, and wind-bitten town.
Then far in the west, as in the beginning,
Dim in the distance, sweet in retreating,
Hark to the *faint*-horn, *quaint*-horn, *saint*-
    horn,
Hark to the *calm*-horn, *balm*-horn, *psalm*-horn. . . .

They are hunting the goals that they under-
    stand:—
San Francisco and the brown sea-sand.
My goal is the mystery the beggars win.

*With a snap-
ping explosive-
ness.*

*To be sung or
read well-nigh
in a whisper.*

*To be bawled
in the begin-
ning with a
snapping
explosiveness,
ending in a
languorous
chant.*

*To be sung to
exactly the
same whis-
pered tune as
the first five
lines.*

*This section
beginning
sonorously,
ending in a
languorous
whisper.*

I am caught in the web the night-winds spin.
The edge of the wheat-ridge speaks to me.
I talk with the leaves of the mulberry tree.
And now I hear, as I sit all alone
In the dusk, by another big Santa-Fé stone,
The souls of the tall corn gathering round
And the gay little souls of the grass in the ground.
Listen to the tale the cottonwood tells.
Listen to the windmills, singing o'er the wells.
Listen to the whistling flutes without price
Of myriad prophets out of paradise.
Harken to the wonder
That the night-air carries. . . .
Listen . . . to . . . the . . . whisper . . .
Of . . . the . . . prairie . . . fairies

    Singing o'er the fairy plain:—
    "Sweet, sweet, sweet, sweet.
    Love and glory,
    Stars and rain,
    Sweet, sweet, sweet, sweet. . . ."

To the same whispered tune as the Rachel-Jane song— but very slowly.

PART IV
NIGHTINGALES

The Chinese Nightingale

A Song in Chinese Tapestries

"How, how," he said. "Friend Chang," I said,
"San Francisco sleeps as the dead—
Ended license, lust and play:
Why do you iron the night away?
Your big clock speaks with a deadly sound,
With a tick and a wail till dawn comes round.
While the monster shadows glower and creep,
What can be better for man than sleep?"

"I will tell you a secret," Chang replied;
"My breast with vision is satisfied,
And I see green trees and fluttering wings,
And my deathless bird from Shanghai sings."
Then he lit five firecrackers in a pan.
"Pop, pop," said the firecrackers, "cra-cra-crack."
He lit a joss stick long and black.
Then the proud gray joss in the corner stirred;
On his wrist appeared a gray small bird,
And this was the song of the gray small bird:
"Where is the princess, loved forever,
Who made Chang first of the kings of men?"

And the joss in the corner stirred again;
And the carved dog, curled in his arms, awoke,
Barked forth a smoke-cloud that whirled and broke.
It piled in a maze round the ironing-place,
And there on the snowy table wide
Stood a Chinese lady of high degree,
With a scornful, witching, tea-rose face. . . .
Yet she put away all form and pride,
And laid her glimmering veil aside
With a childlike smile for Chang and for me.

The walls fell back, night was aflower,
The table gleamed in a moonlit bower,
While Chang, with a countenance carved of stone,
Ironed and ironed, all alone.
And thus she sang to the busy man Chang:
"Have you forgotten . . .
Deep in the ages, long, long ago,
I was your sweetheart, there on the sand—
Storm-worn beach of the Chinese land?
We sold our grain in the peacock town—
Built on the edge of the sea-sands brown—
Built on the edge of the sea-sands brown. . . .

When all the world was drinking blood
From the skulls of men and bulls
And all the world had swords and clubs of stone,
We drank our tea in China beneath the sacred spice-trees,
And heard the curled waves of the harbor moan.
And this gray bird, in Love's first spring,
With a bright-bronze breast and a bronze-brown wing,
Captured the world with his carolling.
Do you remember, ages after,
At last the world we were born to own?
You were the heir of the yellow throne—
The world was the field of the Chinese man
And we were the pride of the Sons of Han?
We copied deep books and we carved in jade,
And wove blue silks in the mulberry shade. . . ."
"I remember, I remember
That Spring came on forever,
That Spring came on forever,"
Said the Chinese nightingale.

My heart was filled with marvel and dream,
Though I saw the western street-lamps gleam,

Though dawn was bringing the western day,
Though Chang was a laundryman ironing away. . . .
Mingled there with the streets and alleys,
The railroad-yard and the clock-tower bright,
Demon clouds crossed ancient valleys;
Across wide lotus-ponds of light
I marked a giant firefly's flight.

And the lady, rosy-red,
Flourished her fan, her shimmering fan,
Stretched her hand toward Chang, and said:
"Do you remember,
Ages after,
Our palace of heart-red stone?
Do you remember
The little doll-faced children
With their lanterns full of moon-fire,
That came from all the empire
Honoring the throne?—
The loveliest fête and carnival
Our world had ever known?
The sages sat about us
With their heads bowed in their beards,
With proper meditation on the sight.
Confucius was not born;
We lived in those great days
Confucius later said were lived aright. . . .
And this gray bird, on that day of spring,
With a bright-bronze breast, and a bronze-brown wing,
Captured the world with his carolling.
Late at night his tune was spent.
Peasants,
Sages,
Children,

Homeward went,
And then the bronze bird sang for you and me.
We walked alone. Our hearts were high and free.
I had a silvery name, I had a silvery name,
I had a silvery name—do you remember
The name you cried beside the tumbling sea?"

Chang turned not to the lady slim—
He bent to his work, ironing away;
But she was arch, and knowing and glowing,
For the bird on his shoulder spoke for him.

"Darling . . . darling . . . darling . . . darling . . ."
Said the Chinese nightingale.

The great gray joss on the rustic shelf,
Rakish and shrewd, with his collar awry,
Sang impolitely, as though by himself,
Drowning with his bellowing the nightingale's cry:
"Back through a hundred, hundred years
Hear the waves as they climb the piers,
Hear the howl of the silver seas,
Hear the thunder.
Hear the gongs of holy China
How the waves and tunes combine
In a rhythmic clashing wonder,
Incantation old and fine:
    'Dragons, dragons, Chinese dragons,
    Red firecrackers, and green firecrackers
    And dragons, dragons, Chinese dragons.' "

Then the lady, rosy-red,
Turned to her lover Chang and said:
"Dare you forget that turquoise dawn

When we stood in our mist-hung velvet lawn,
And worked a spell this great joss taught
Till a God of the Dragons was charmed and caught?
From the flag high over our palace home
He flew to our feet in rainbow-foam—
A king of beauty and tempest and thunder
Panting to tear our sorrows asunder.
A dragon of fair adventure and wonder.
We mounted the back of that royal slave
With thoughts of desire that were noble and grave.
We swam down the shore to the dragon-mountains,
We whirled to the peaks and the fiery fountains.
To our secret ivory house we were borne.
We looked down the wonderful wing-filled regions
Where the dragons darted in glimmering legions.
Right by my breast the nightingale sang;
The old rhymes rang in the sunlit mist
That we this hour regain—
Song-fire for the brain.
When my hands and my hair and my feet you kissed,
When you cried for your heart's new pain,
What was my name in the dragon-mist,
In the rings of rainbowed rain?"

"Sorrow and love, glory and love,"
Said the Chinese nightingale.
"Sorrow and love, glory and love,"
Said the Chinese nightingale.

And now the joss broke in with his song:
"Dying ember, bird of Chang,
Soul of Chang, do you remember?—
Ere you returned to the shining harbor
There were pirates by ten thousand

Descended on the town
In vessels mountain-high and red and brown,
Moon-ships that climbed the storms and cut the skies.
On their prows were painted terrible bright eyes.
But I was then a wizard and a scholar and a priest;
I stood upon the sand;
With lifted hand I looked upon them
And sunk their vessels with my wizard eyes,
And the stately lacquer-gate made safe again.
Deep, deep below the bay, the seaweed and the spray,
Embalmed in amber every pirate lies,
Embalmed in amber every pirate lies."

Then this did the noble lady say:
"Bird, do you dream of our home-coming day
When you flew like a courier on before
From the dragon-peak to our palace-door,
And we drove the steed in your singing path—
The ramping dragon of laughter and wrath:
And found our city all aglow,
And knighted this joss that decked it so?
There were golden fishes in the purple river
And silver fishes and rainbow fishes.
There were golden junks in the laughing river,
And silver junks and rainbow junks:
There were golden lilies by the bay and river,
And silver lilies and tiger-lilies,
And tinkling wind-bells in the gardens of the town
By the black-lacquer gate
Where walked in state
The kind king Chang
And his sweetheart mate. . . .
With his flag-born dragon
And his crown of pearl . . . and . . . jade,

And his nightingale reigning in the mulberry shade,
And sailors and soldiers on the sea-sands brown,
And priests who bowed them down to your song—
By the city called Han, the peacock town,
By the city called Han, the nightingale town,
The nightingale town."

Then sang the bird, so strangely gay,
Fluttering, fluttering, ghostly and gray,
A vague, unravelling, final tune,
Like a long unwinding silk cocoon;
Sang as though for the soul of him
Who ironed away in that bower dim:—
  "I have forgotten
  Your dragons great,
  Merry and mad and friendly and bold.
Dim is your proud lost palace-gate.
I vaguely know
There were heroes of old,
Troubles more than the heart could hold,
There were wolves in the woods
Yet lambs in the fold,
Nests in the top of the almond tree. . . .
The evergreen tree . . . and the mulberry tree . . .
Life and hurry and joy forgotten,
Years on years I but half-remember . . .
Man is a torch, then ashes soon,
May and June, then dead December,
Dead December, then again June.
Who shall end my dream's confusion?
Life is a loom, weaving illusion . . .
I remember, I remember
There were ghostly veils and laces . . .
In the shadowy bowery places . . .

With lovers' ardent faces
Bending to one another,
Speaking each his part.
They infinitely echo
In the red cave of my heart.
'Sweetheart, sweetheart, sweetheart,'
They said to one another.
They spoke, I think, of perils past.
They spoke, I think, of peace at last.
One thing I remember:
Spring came on forever,
Spring came on forever,"
Said the Chinese nightingale.

The Flower of Mending

(To Eudora, after I had had certain dire adventures)

When Dragon-fly would fix his wings,
When Snail would patch his house,
When moths have marred the overcoat
Of tender Mister Mouse,

The pretty creatures go with haste
To the sunlit blue-grass hills
Where the Flower of Mending yields the wax
And webs to help their ills.

The hour the coats are waxed and webbed
They fall into a dream,
And when they wake the ragged robes
Are joined without a seam.

My heart is but a dragon-fly,
My heart is but a mouse,
My heart is but a haughty snail
In a little stony house.

Your hand was honey-comb to heal,
Your voice a web to bind.
You were a Mending Flower to me
To cure my heart and mind.

Sunshine

(For a very little girl, not a year old)

CATHERINE FRAZEE WAKEFIELD

The sun gives not directly
   The coal, the diamond crown;
Not in a special basket
   Are these from Heaven let down.

The sun gives not directly
   The plough, man's iron friend;
Not by a path or stairway
   Do tools from Heaven descend.

Yet sunshine fashions all things
   That cut or burn or fly;
And corn that seems upon the earth
   Is made in the hot sky.

The gravel of the roadbed,
   The metal of the gun,
The engine of the airship
   Trace somehow from the sun.

And so your soul, my lady
   (Mere sunshine, nothing more),
Prepares me the contraptions
   I work with or adore.

Within me cornfields rustle,
   Niagaras roar their way,
Vast thunderstorms and rainbows
   Are in my thought today.

Ten thousand anvils sound there
  By forges flaming white,
And many books I read there,
  And many books I write;

And freedom's bells are ringing,
  And bird-choirs chant and fly—
The whole world works in me today
  And all the shining sky,

Because of one small lady
  Whose smile is my chief sun.
She gives not any gift to me
  Yet all gifts, giving one. . . .

                              Amen.

Z

WITHDRAWN